Sneaky Pete

Mr Cross looked in the tank.
“I can’t see Pete,” he said.

The children looked in the tank.
They could see Pete.

SUPER SNAKES

Contents

Dee Reid

Story illustrated by Charlie Fowkes

Heinemann

Before Reading

In this story

Mr Cross

The children

Pete the python

Tricky words

- tank
- children
- could
- under
- toilet
- silly

Introduce these tricky words and help the reader when they come across them later!

Story starter

Mr Cross was a teacher. One day, he took the children to the zoo. They went to see Pete the python. Mr Cross looked in the tank, but he couldn't see Pete.

"Help!" said Mr Cross.
"Pete is not here!"

The children could see Pete but they didn't tell Mr Cross.

"Help me to look for Pete,"
said Mr Cross.

Mr Cross looked under the tank but he could not see Pete.

He looked in the toilet
but he could not see Pete.
Where will Pete
go next?

"Look!" said the children.
"Pete is in the tank."

Mr Cross looked in the tank.

He could see Pete.

"Silly me!" said Mr Cross.
"Pete was in the tank
all the time."

Quiz

Text Detective

- Was Pete in the tank all the time?
- Why do you think this story is called 'Sneaky Pete'?

Word Detective

- **Phonic Focus**: Initial letter sounds
  Page 12: Find two words that begin with 't'.
- Page 5: Find a word that rhymes with 'hot'.
- Pages 8-9: Find the word 'could' twice.

Super Speller

Read these words:

see but to

Now try to spell them!

HA! HA! HA!

Q What do you call a snake without any clothes on?

A S-naked!

Before Reading

Find out about

- How snakes kill their prey

Tricky words

- poison
- use
- prey
- bite
- squeeze
- chew
- swallow

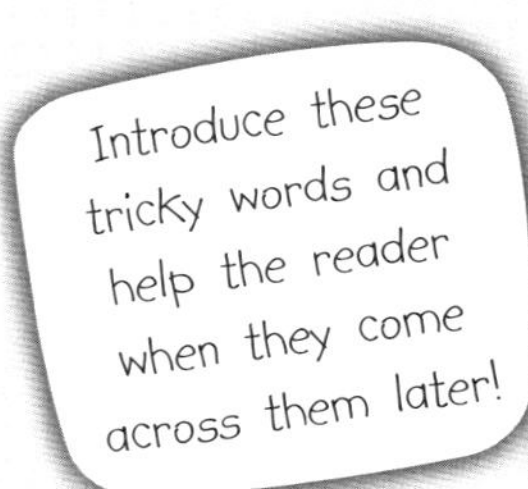

Text starter

There are lots of different sorts of snakes and some of them are huge! Not all snakes use poison to kill their prey. Some snakes squeeze their prey to death. Some snakes, however, make very good pets!

Snake Bites

Some snakes are big.
Some snakes are very big.
Some snakes are
very, very big!

Some big snakes have poison.
They use poison to kill their prey.
The poison is called venom.

They bite their prey to kill it.

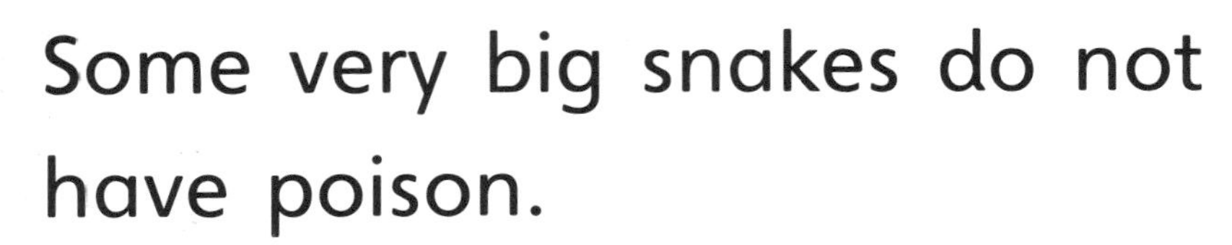

Some very big snakes do not have poison.

They squeeze their prey to kill it.

They squeeze and squeeze their prey.

They do not chew their prey.
They swallow it.

Some very, very big snakes swallow very big prey!

Some snakes make very good pets.

A pet snake is lots of fun!

Quiz

Text Detective

- Do snakes chew their prey?
- Would you like a snake as a pet?

Word Detective

- **Phonic Focus**: Initial letter sounds

  Page 16: Find a word that begins with 'b'.
- Page 19: Find the word 'they' twice.
- Page 22: Find a word that rhymes with 'come'.

Super Speller

Read these words:

and it of

Now try to spell them!

HA! HA! HA!

Q What does a snake like best at school?

Hissstory!